YOGI and YOGETTE
learn the
ASANA ALPHABET

26 yoga poses
to learn and color with
bonus teacher and caretaker index

conceived by Ann Robideaux
designed by Michela Muserra

Asana Alphabet Press
ISBN: 0-9771163-0-1

WARNING!

The exercises and yoga postures described in this book are meant as an extra learning device and are not intended to take the place of a class by a trained yoga teacher. Please use extreme caution when performing any pose and consult a physician before exploring any exercise program. The designers, makers, writers and others involved with Asana Alphabet™ do not claim responsibility for any injury suffered through the use of this book or yoga program.

Dedicated to all teachers and students past and present.

AIM AN ARROW IN ARCHER POSE

BREATHE IN BOW POSE

COLOR ME COBRA &
HISS LIKE A SNAKE

DAZZLE IN DANCER POSE

PERCH LIKE AN EAGLE

FLOAT LIKE A FISH

GRAB HANDS IN GOMUKHASANA

HANG YOUR FEET OVER YOUR
HEAD IN HALASANA

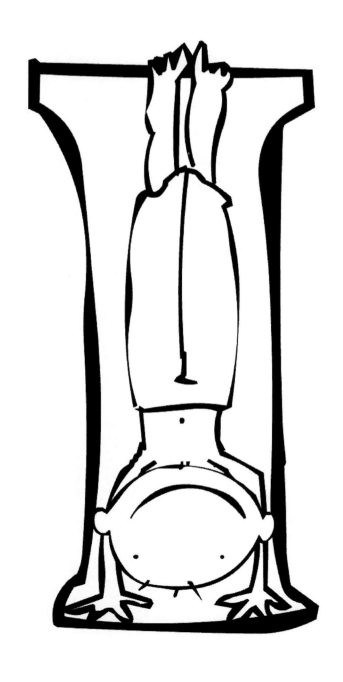

INSIDE OUT - UPSIDE DOWN
INVERSION

JOIN HEAD TO KNEE IN
JANUSURSASANA

KURMASANA IS SANSKRIT FOR
TURTLE

ROAR LIKE A LION

MINDFULLY MEDITATE

FLOAT LIKE A BOAT IN
NAVASANA

OPEN FOR AN OM

PUSH-UP IN PLANK

SHHH. . .YOU'LL BE CALM WHEN
YOU'RE QUIET

REST AND RELAX

SURE YOU CAN SHOULDERSTAND

TRY TO BALANCE IN TREE

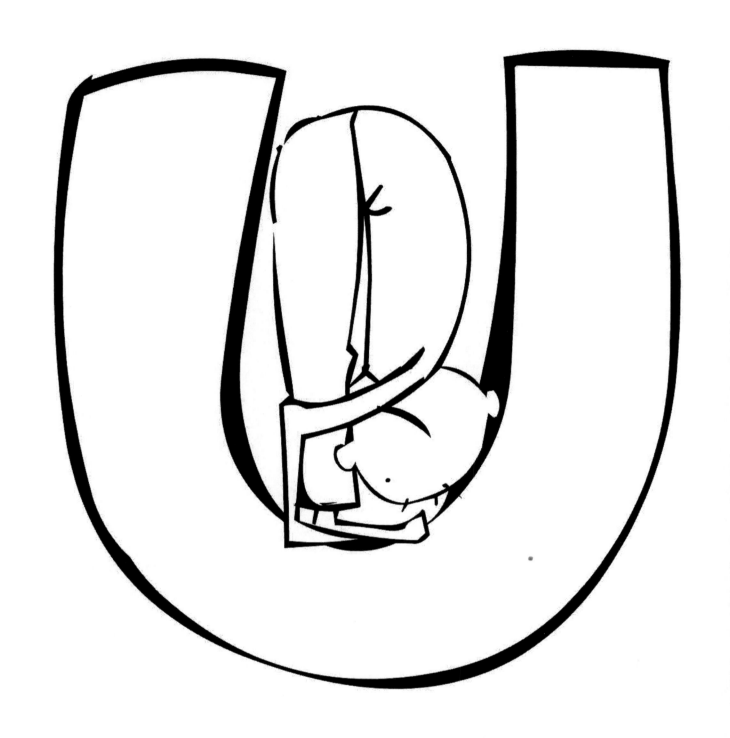

UPSIDE DOWN IN UTTANASANA

VICTORY IN VIRABHADRASANA

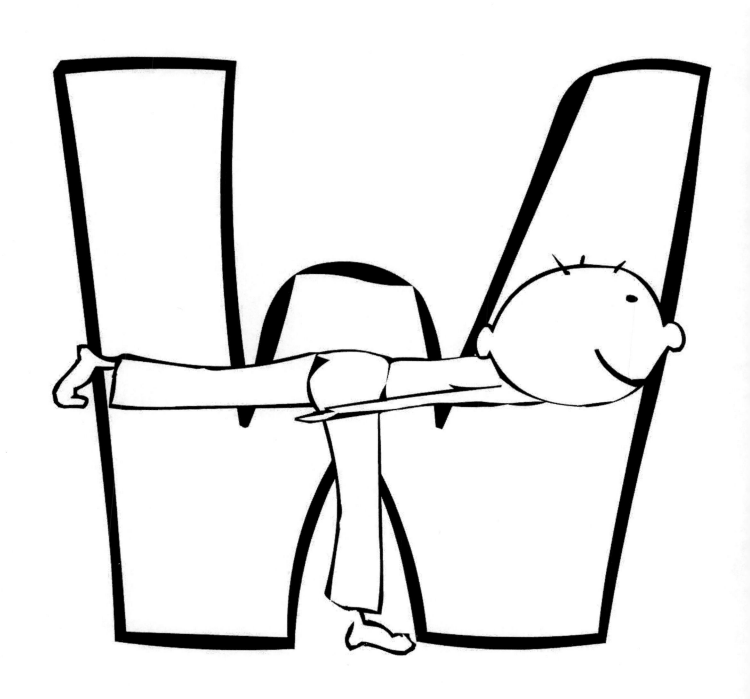

WIN LIKE A WARRIOR

X-ERCISE

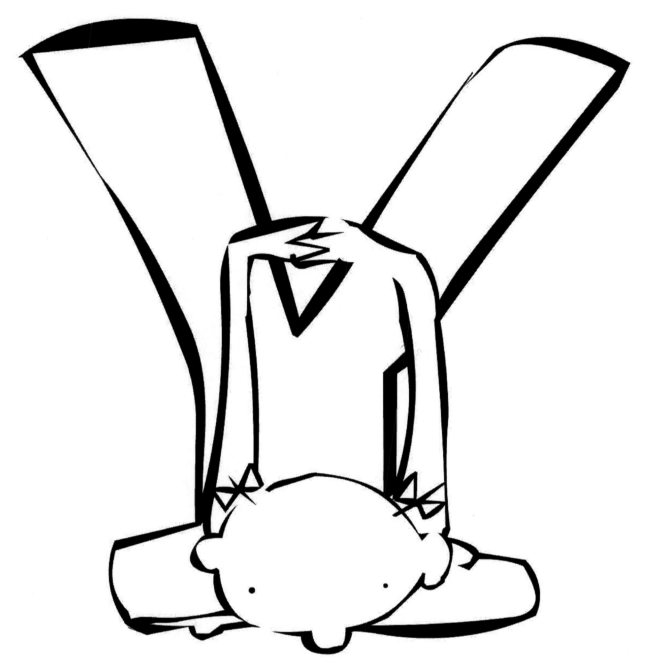

YOGETTE SITS IN YOGA MUDRA

SQUIGGLE INTO A ZIG ZAG

ASANA ALPHABET INDEX

Archer Pose: Lunge with your right leg bent parallel to the floor in front and the left leg straight in back. Keep right arm straight and parallel to the ground with your index finger touching your thumb. Pull the left arm back as if pulling back on a bow and arrow. Strengthens and tones. Repeat on the other side.

Bow pose: Lie on your stomach with your forehead on the ground. Bend your knees so your toes face the ceiling. Reach back for the right ankle with your right hand and the left ankle with your left hand. Press your ankles into your hands to lift your body into an arch. Good for opening all the chakras and the entire body. Take it slow. You may want to practice cobra with your feet up first.

Cobra: Lie on your stomach. Bring your legs close together and parallel to the floor. Place your hands underneath your shoulders. Press into your hands to arch and lengthen your spine, avoiding any "crunching"of the back. Opens the spine and strengthens arm & back muscles.

Dancer: Standing firm on your right leg, lift the left foot behind you and grab onto the ankle or top of the foot with the left hand. With right arm straight in front of you, take a long deep breath and then press the left foot into the left hand to arch the back. Reverse sides. Opens the torso, works on balance and tones the working leg.

Eagle: Standing on your right leg, lift your left knee up as high as possible. Wind the left leg over the right thigh with the left foot around the right calf. Place your elbows together, right one on top, and wind the arms so the palms touch. Good for releasing tight hips and shoulders and working on balance.

Fish Pose: Lie flat on your back with you legs together parallel. Bend your arms and bring your elbows next to your rib cage. Lift your chest towards the sky and tilt the top of the head towards the floor.

Ghomukasana: Cross the right leg over the left at the knee joint, bend the knees and try to sit between your feet (or simply sit on your knees). Bring your left hand over your left shoulder and down the back as you reach the right arm around the right waist and behind you. Try to hold hands with yourself. Opens the shoulders and hips.

<u>Halasana</u>: Also known as "plough pose". Lie down on your back, lifting your feet up into the air. Keeping the spine and neck in a straight line, sweep the hips up and the feet over the head towards the floor. The ultimate back stretch and hamstring stretch.   Do slowly and with caution.

<u>Inversion</u>: To turn upside down in a handstand, keep your arms as straight as possible, shoulders and hips in line with one another, belly strong. You can use the help of a capable adult to hold your legs or use a wall for support behind you. Please exercise extreme caution with any inversion.

<u>Janusirsasana</u>: Head-to-knee pose. Sitting with the left leg straight and the foot flexed, bring the right sole of the foot to the inside of the left thigh. Fold your torso over your legs. Slowly release and switch sides. For toning the internal organs and stretching the sciatic nerve.

<u>Kurmasana</u>: Also known as turtle pose. Sit with the spine tall and your legs 60 degrees away from one another in a straddle. Lift the knees and thread your arms under the same-side leg. Breathe and open your torso towards the floor. Eventually the legs will straighten. Works on flexibility.

<u>Lion</u>: Sit on your knees, spread your hands wide like lion paws, stick your tongue out as far as you can and roar like a lion 2-6 times. This facilitates a positive mood and detoxifies the body.

<u>Meditation</u>: Sitting in a comfortable cross-legged posture with the spine tall, close the eyes and look up to your brow point. Your hands can rest on the knees. Focus on your. Clears the mind and a plethora of other benefits.

<u>Navasana</u>: Sit with your legs out in front of you and your hands behind you. Rock back so the legs come 60 degrees off the ground. Reach your arms parallel to the floor. Tones the abdominals.

<u>Om</u>: Sitting as in meditation, inhale deeply and chant a long OM to the end of the exhale. Repeat several times. For mental focus, clarity and bliss.

<u>Plank Pose</u>: Bring your body into a preliminary push-up posture with the elbows straight, hands and toes on the floor with the spine and head in one long diagonal line. Tones arms and abs.

<u>Quiet</u>: Keep your mind quiet for greater awareness.

ASANA ALPHABET INDEX CONTINUED

<u>Rest</u>: Always take rest on the back in corpse pose, or sivasana, after yoga practice. Lie on your back, close your eyes, keep your arms by your sides with the palms facing up. Deeply relax. 1-10 minutes.

<u>Shoulder Stand</u>: Lying on your back, raise your legs straight with the feet to the ceiling. Rock the hips up and back as your hands catch your back. Lift your feet high until you are "standing" on your shoulders. Use caution and do not turn your head in the posture.

<u>Tree pose</u>: Standing on your right leg, lift the left foot to the inside of the right thigh and the hands together in prayer mudra. Keep the eyes steady on one point. Hold for 5-10 breaths and switch sides.

<u>Uttanasana</u>: Or standing forward bend. Stand with your legs firm and your feet parallel. Bring the big toes to touch one another. Bending from the hip joints, lengthen your spine forward. If back or hamstrings are tight, bend the knees; otherwise, lengthen the hips up to the sky and hold onto to your elbows, the backs of the calves or the big toes. Stretches the back, legs and lengthens the spine.

<u>Virabhadrasana I</u>: Also known as Warrior I, stand in a lunge position with the front leg bent and the back leg straight. Lift the arms towards the sky and bring the palms to touch each other. Victory!

<u>Warrior III</u>: Keep your right leg straight as you tilt forward from the hip joint and lift your left leg. Your left ankle is flexed with the toes pointing towards the floor. For balance and overcoming obstacles.

<u>X</u>: Begin in a squat and jump out to form a letter X with your body. Repeat 10-20 times. Done quickly enough, it will create an aerobic component to your yoga routine.

<u>Yoga Mudra</u>: Sit cross-legged. Hold hands with yourself, interlacing the fingers behind your back. Inhale deeply and then fold the torso over the legs, reaching the head towards the floor on an exhale. Opens the shoulders and hips and facilitates a meditative mind.

<u>Zig Zag</u>: From plank pose, bend the knees to the floor, reach the chest and chin to the floor. Elbows parallel to the ribcage and the hips lifted up. Release gently through cobra pose.

Asana Alphabet™

Review!

A is for _____

B is for _____

C is for _____

D is for _____

E is for _____

F is for _____

G is for _____

H is for _____

I is for _____

J is for _____

K is for _____

L is for _____

M is for _____

N is for _____

O is for _____

P is for _____

Q is for _____

R is for _____

S is for _____

T is for _____

U is for _____

V is for _____

W is for _____

X is for _____

Y is for _____

Z is for _____